DALER ◆ ROWNEY

Art Therapy
Fashion

Mode
Mode
Moda
Moda

Art-thérapie · Kunsttherapie · Terapia artistica · Terapia d'arte

This fine selection of designs is the fruit of a partnership between

Cette sélection de dessins est le fruit d'une collaboration entre
Die feine Auswahl an Zeichnungen entstand aus der Zusammenarbeit von
Esta magnífica selección de diseños es el fruto de una colaboración entre
Questa bella selezione di disegni e' resultato di un' alleanza tra

DALER ◆ ROWNEY

&

Liloye Duperrier

D1442760

DALER ◆ ROWNEY

Art Therapy
Fashion
Mode
Mode
Moda
Moda

(GB) Colouring is not just for kids anymore: the therapeutic effects of colouring lend themselves to a multi-generational appeal. Free your mind of all the stresses of your daily routine and immerse yourself in hours of meditative wellness. People of all ages are rediscovering this simple activity as the perfect way to relax, while stimulating their inner creative expression. These books make art easy - find your favorite!

(F) Le coloriage n'est plus réservé qu'aux enfants : les effets thérapeutiques du coloriage s'adressent à toutes les générations. Libérez votre esprit du stress quotidien en vous plongeant plusieurs heures dans cette activité de méditation. Des personnes de tous âges redécouvrent une manière simple et agréable de se détendre, tout en stimulant leur créativité.   Ces livres sont conçus pour vous inspirer, choisissez votre favori!

(D) Ausmalen ist nicht mehr nur für Kinder: die therapeutische Wirkung des Ausmalens greift längst auf alle Generationen über. Befreien Sie Sich vom Alltagsstress und tauchen Sie ein in Stunden meditativer Wellness für Ihren Kopf. Menschen aller Altersgruppen entdecken diese einfache Entspannungsmöglichkeit wieder, die währenddessen die individuelle Kreativität anregt. Finden Sie mit Ihrem Lieblingsbuch ganz leicht Ihren Weg zur Kunst!

(E) Colorear ya no es solo para niños: los efectos terapeúticos que proporciona colorear atraen a gente de todas las edades. Libere su mente de todos los estreses de su rutina diaria y sumérjase en horas de meditación para el bienestar. Gente de todas las edades están redescubriendo esta simple actividad como la forma perfecta para relajarse mientras estimulan su creatividad interior. Estos libros hacen el arte fácil, ¡encuentre su favorito!

(I) Colorare non e' piu' solo per bambini: L'effetto terapiutico del colorare attiva diverse generazioni. Liberati la mente dallo stress quotidiano e immergiti in ore di benessere meditativo. Persone do ogni et'a riscoprono questa semplice attivita' per rilassarsi e' stimolare un' espressione creativa. Questi libri rendono l'arte facile. Trova ie tuo favorito.

DALER ◆ ROWNEY

(GB) Liloye Duperrier is a French aspiring designer residing in New York City, the city where dreams come true. She is currently studying at the Fashion Institute of Technology (FIT) and hopes to pursue her dream of fashion design.

(F) Liloye Duperrier est une créatrice française résidant à New-York, la ville où les rêves deviennent réalité. Elle étudie actuellement à l'Institut des Techniques de la Mode et espère poursuivre son rêve dans la création de mode.

(D) Liloye Duperrier ist eine aufstrebende, französische Designerin in New York City, die Stadt in der Träume wahr werden. Zur Zeit studiert sie am Fashion Institute of Technology (FIT) und hofft ihren Traum von Fashion Design verwirklichen zu können.

(E) Liloye Duperrier es una aspirante a diseñadora que vive en la ciudad de Nueva York, la ciudad donde los sueños se hacen realidad. Actualmente está estudiando en el Instituto Tecnológico de la Moda (FIT) y espera poder perseguir su sueño de diseño de moda.

(I) Liloye Duperrier e' un Francese che aspira ad essere disegnatore e vivere a New York, la citta dove si avverano I sogni. Al momento studia a F.I.T. e spera di perseguire il suo sogno di Disegno Moda.

Art Therapy Fashion
Mode
Mode
Moda
Moda

www.daler-rowney.com